Grandpa and the Truck

Tales by a Long-Haul Trucker

Colleen Kelly Mellor
Illustrations by Dana M. Irwin

BOOK ONE

This book is dedicated

to our three little

trucker grandsons—

Luke, Finn, and Sam

and all future truckers

out there.

Published by truckerkidzpress

Warwick, Rhode Island

Cover illustration by Dana M. Irwin

Book and cover design by Dana M. Irwin

Manufactured in U.S.A.

10 9 8 7 6 5 4 3 2 1

First Edition

Library of Congress Cataloging-in-publication Data

Mellor, Colleen Kelly

ISBN 978-0-9856770-0-8

Hello, Little Trucker Buddies....

I'm "Grandpa" now, but I was long-haul trucker Paul Gates—trucker buddies called me "Gater." I carted household goods across the country for 30 years.

Yep, I was one of those on the highway in the big rigs, sitting high above everybody else.

I know you little guys love our trucks because you get excited when you see us and wave to us. Our trucks excite us, too. That's one reason we went into this business.

In this job, we meet fascinating people, travel all over, and overcome difficult problems of bad road conditions, crazy drivers, and awful weather.

Now, I invite you little truckers to come along with me on the journey, to see what it's like being a trucker.

So, climb up the steps, hop in, and buckle up. I promise you—
The ride will be interesting....

The Stories and Their Lessons

1

It's Not Always Wise to Follow the Leader

Grandpa drove his truck all over this country and on those trips, he saw some pretty interesting sights. One time he was driving

his big rig through a mountain pass on route 101 ,
in California. It was the beginning of a 10-hour trip.
Suddenly, he noticed one of a trucker's worst fears—fog!

It was getting thicker and thicker.

As Grandpa described it, “That fog was so thick that if I stood outside and held my hand up, I couldn‘t see it.”

Now, that fog was acting like fog always does—it hugged the mountains low, making visibility difficult. Truckers know how dangerous that is because no one can see the roadway very well.

Luckily, Grandpa was above the fog because he sat high in the big truck, so he could see what was happening all around him.

Up ahead, he noticed a “smokie” (a policeman) with an antenna whip rising high over his car. The whip was clearly visible to all, since it danced above the fog.

And Grandpa saw cars lining up to follow the “smokie”, watching for his antenna. They figured somehow that policeman could see better than they could.

In other words, they were using the “smokie” and his car antenna as guides to get them through the fog.

And then, an interesting thing happened. Suddenly the road split, and the “smokie” went to the right. But he must have gotten confused because he turned too much.

Next, his patrol car split the guardrail and rolled down into a deep ditch, landing on a pile of rocks.

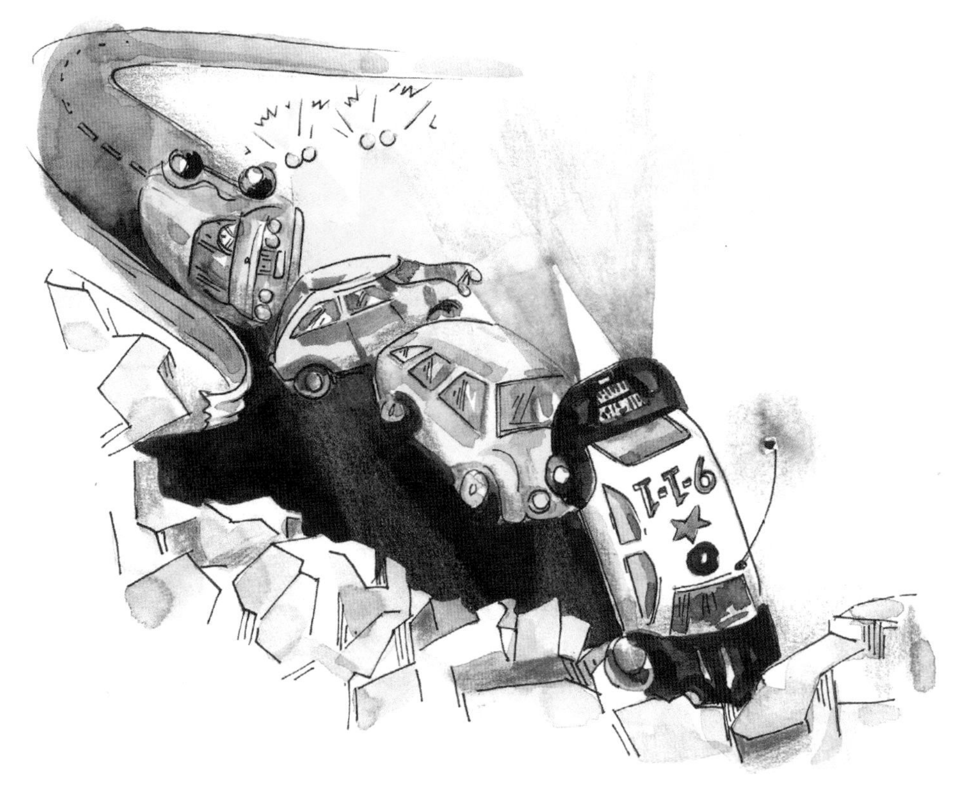

What happened to the other cars following him? They went there, too, crashing into his car and into each other. Five or six of them piled up in the wreckage.

Grandpa watched it all happen from his big rig. He didn't stop (because that would cause more of a mess), but he called 911 on his CB radio to report it, saying "Breaker, breaker 1...9. This is 'Gater'. There's been an accident on US Highway 101, heading north, near mile marker 146. Several cars followed a police car right off the highway, into a ditch."

No one was seriously hurt that day,
but they all learned a valuable lesson...

It's not always wise
to follow the leader,
for if the leader
goes wrong,
everyone else
goes wrong
with him.

It's Not Always Wise to Follow the Leader

QUESTIONS AND TRUCKER TERMS

1. Find the location of Grandpa and the truck on the California map on page 30. In what direction—north, south, east or west—was the truck heading? (((●)) = where the truck is)

2. What's one of a trucker's greatest fears—in this story? Why?

3. Why shouldn't you stop to help another car in the fog?

4. What should you do, if you see an accident?

5. What's the main lesson in the story?

TRUCKER TERMS IN THIS STORY:

BIG RIG: 18-wheeler, trailer truck

"SMOKIE": policeman

POLICE CRUISER: "smokie's" car

CB RADIO: special radio all truckers have

NOTE
When truckers say "Breaker…breaker…1..9" they're asking permission to "break" into the conversation other truckers are having on channel 19 on their CB radios. Truckers all have "handles" or names other truckers call them. Grandpa's was "Gater."

2
Ralph and the Bloodhounds

Sometimes, Grandpa drove his big rig with a partner and Ralph was one of his favorites. Together, they logged many miles and shared many experiences. One night, in particular, stands out in his memory.

Grandpa and Ralph were coming back from New Orleans, going north to New England, along Route 11 in Virginia, passing farmlands and fields. The scenery along that stretch of road is really beautiful...

But because it was late, Grandpa could barely make out the outline of the Blue Ridge Mountains in the distance.He knew that soon it would be dark.

Ralph wouldn't have seen those mountains anyway, for he was sleeping. He'd driven earlier in the day.

Grandpa had been looking for a truck stop on that lonely stretch of road, and he was having no luck. He finally pulled into a darkened station and looked around for the owner but saw no one...just a house with a light on, up the hill behind the station.

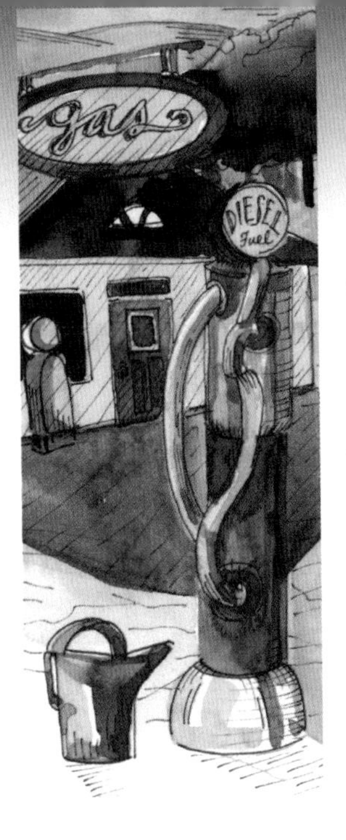

Grandpa saw diesel pumps—just the kind of fuel he needed. He nudged Ralph, saying, "Hey, Ralph…wake up. I need you to go up the hill behind the station, and get the owner to come down and sell us some fuel. We're almost out." Grandpa's plan was to stay with the truck.

Ralph stretched and yawned and then hopped down from the truck. He looked up the hill, saw the light, and said, "OK, I'll be back in a few." He then headed into the darkness.

In the next several minutes, Grandpa heard a mighty howling and barking of dogs. They sounded like bloodhounds, the kind of dogs Grandpa used for tracking, when he was growing up in Arkansas.

Next, Grandpa made out the figure of Ralph, in the moonlight, running down the trail, through the woods, towards the truck, yelling, "Quick...Open the door, Paul...they're after me!!"

Grandpa swung open the door just in time, for the dogs were hot on Ralph's heels, ready to take a chunk out of his butt. He just made it to the truck ahead of the dogs, jumped up on the steps, swung onto the seat, and slammed the door. He only barely escaped.

Poor Ralph. He thought he was just going up to get the gas station owner when, instead, he came flying down a hilly path, followed by pack of the owner's dogs.

Some minutes later, the owner came down and pumped the diesel fuel Grandpa needed. But Grandpa and Ralph learned from this experience that:

It's never a good idea to walk off into unfamiliar territory, alone, for there's no telling what you'll meet up with.

Ralph and the Bloodhounds

QUESTIONS AND TRUCKER TERMS

1. Find the spot on the Virginia map, on page 31, where the truck is.
2. In what direction—east, west, north, south—is the truck headed?
   (((●)) = where the truck is)
3. Why was Ralph sleeping in the truck while Grandpa drove?
4. What's the fuel that trucks need? (hint—it's not gas)
5. How did Grandpa know what dogs Ralph met up with, just from hearing them?
6. What's the lesson from this story?
7. Can you apply this lesson to other areas of your life (where else should you be careful about going?)

TRUCKER TERMS IN THIS STORY:

DIESEL: fuel for trucks

Congratulations, little trucker buddy....
Now, you're beginning to talk like a trucker!

CALIFORNIA

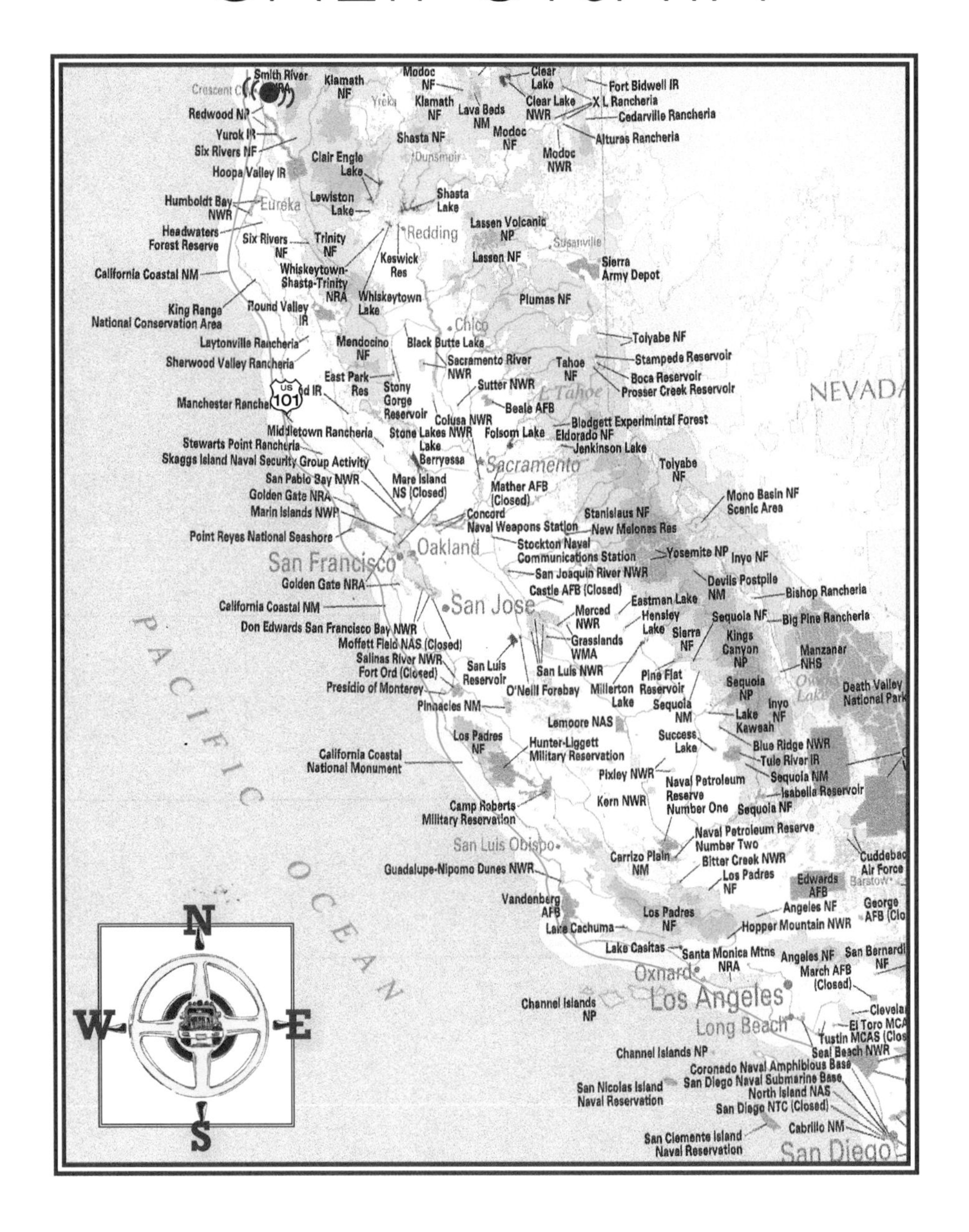
Smith River NRA
Crescent City
Klamath NF
Modoc NF
Clear Lake
Fort Bidwell IR
Redwood NP
Yreka
Klamath NF
Lava Beds NM
Clear Lake NWR
X L Rancheria
Cedarville Rancheria
Yurok IR
Six Rivers NF
Shasta NF
Modoc NF
Alturas Rancheria
Hoopa Valley IR
Clair Engle Lake
Dunsmuir
Modoc NWR
Humboldt Bay NWR
Eureka
Lewiston Lake
Shasta Lake
Headwaters Forest Reserve
Six Rivers NF
Trinity NF
Redding
Lassen Volcanic NP
Susanville
California Coastal NM
Whiskeytown-Shasta-Trinity NRA
Keswick Res
Lassen NF
Sierra Army Depot
King Range National Conservation Area
Round Valley IR
Whiskeytown Lake
Plumas NF
Chico
Laytonville Rancheria
Mendocino NF
Black Butte Lake
Toiyabe NF
Sherwood Valley Rancheria
Sacramento River NWR
Tahoe NF
Stampede Reservoir
Boca Reservoir
Prosser Creek Reservoir
East Park Res
Stony Gorge Reservoir
Sutter NWR
L. Tahoe
NEVADA
Manchester Rancheria
US 101
Beale AFB
Colusa NWR
Blodgett Experimintal Forest
Middletown Rancheria
Stone Lakes NWR
Folsom Lake
Eldorado NF
Stewarts Point Rancheria
Lake Berryessa
Jenkinson Lake
Skaggs Island Naval Security Group Activity
Sacramento
Toiyabe NF
San Pablo Bay NWR
Mare Island NS (Closed)
Mather AFB (Closed)
Golden Gate NRA
Mono Basin NF Scenic Area
Marin Islands NWR
Concord Naval Weapons Station
Stanislaus NF
New Melones Res
Point Reyes National Seashore
Oakland
Stockton Naval Communications Station
Yosemite NP
Inyo NF
San Francisco
San Joaquin River NWR
Devils Postpile NM
Golden Gate NRA
Castle AFB (Closed)
Eastman Lake
Bishop Rancheria
California Coastal NM
San Jose
Merced NWR
Hensley Lake
Sequoia NF
Big Pine Rancheria
Don Edwards San Francisco Bay NWR
Sierra NF
Kings Canyon NP
Grasslands WMA
Manzanar NHS
Moffett Field NAS (Closed)
Salinas River NWR
San Luis Reservoir
San Luis NWR
Pine Flat Reservoir
Fort Ord (Closed)
Sequoia NP
Owens Lake
Death Valley National Park
Presidio of Monterey
O'Neill Forebay
Millerton Lake
Sequoia NM
Inyo NF
Pinnacles NM
Lake Kaweah
Lemoore NAS
Los Padres NF
Success Lake
Hunter-Liggett Military Reservation
Blue Ridge NWR
California Coastal National Monument
Tule River IR
Pixley NWR
Naval Petroleum Reserve Number One
Sequoia NM
Isabella Reservoir
Kern NWR
Sequoia NF
Camp Roberts Military Reservation
Naval Petroleum Reserve Number Two
San Luis Obispo
Carrizo Plain NM
Bitter Creek NWR
Guadalupe-Nipomo Dunes NWR
Los Padres NF
Edwards AFB
Barstow
Vandenberg AFB
Los Padres NF
Angeles NF
George AFB
Lake Cachuma
Hopper Mountain NWR
Lake Casitas
Santa Monica Mtns NRA
Angeles NF
San Bernardino NF
Oxnard
March AFB (Closed)
PACIFIC OCEAN
Channel Islands NP
Los Angeles
Long Beach
El Toro MCAS
Tustin MCAS
Seal Beach NWR
Channel Islands NP
Coronado Naval Amphibious Base
San Diego Naval Submarine Base
San Nicolas Island Naval Reservation
North Island NAS
San Diego NTC (Closed)
San Clemente Island Naval Reservation
Cabrillo NM
San Diego
N
W
E
S

VIRGINIA

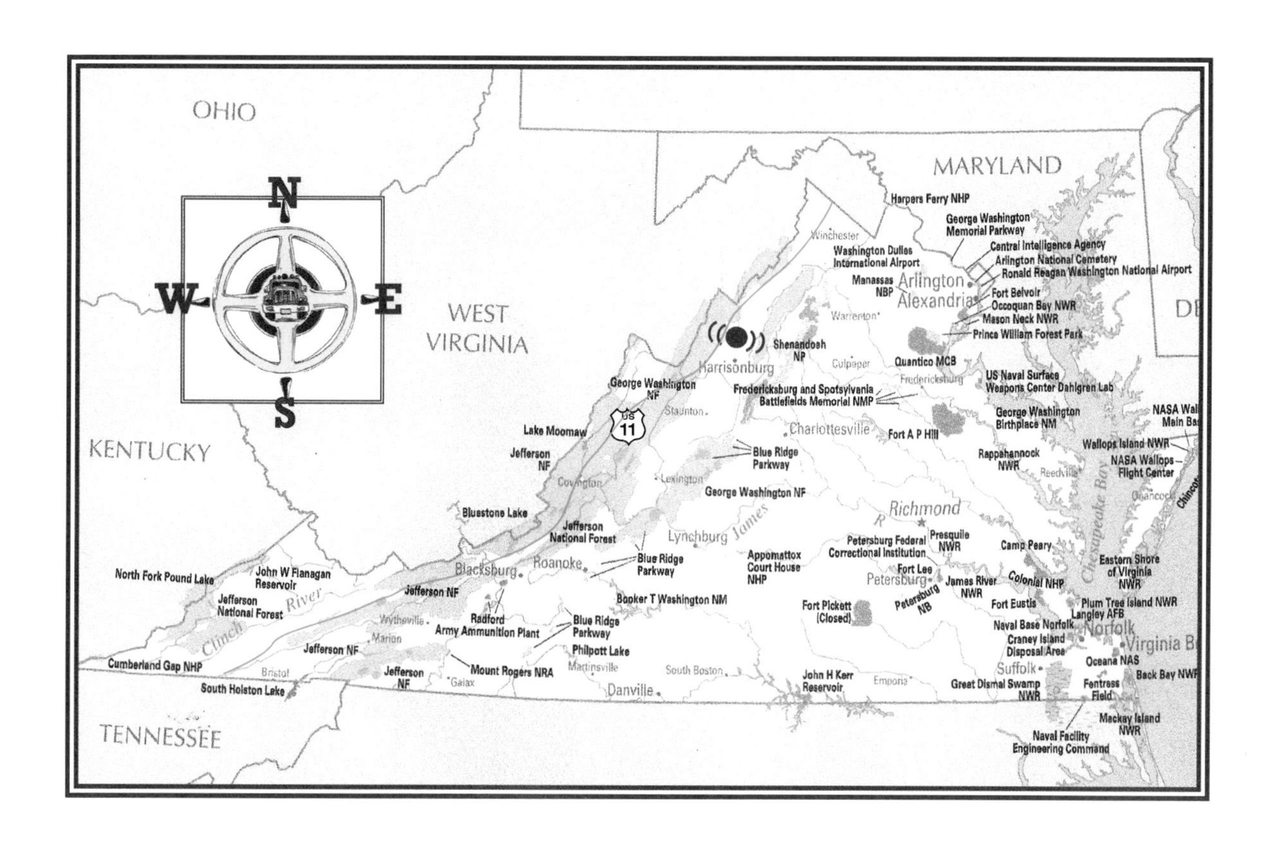

OHIO
MARYLAND
WEST VIRGINIA
KENTUCKY
TENNESSEE
N
W
E
S
US 11
Harpers Ferry NHP
George Washington Memorial Parkway
Central Intelligence Agency
Arlington National Cemetery
Ronald Reagan Washington National Airport
Washington Dulles International Airport
Manassas NBP
Arlington
Alexandria
Fort Belvoir
Occoquan Bay NWR
Mason Neck NWR
Prince William Forest Park
Winchester
Warrenton
Shenandoah NP
Harrisonburg
Culpeper
Quantico MCB
Fredericksburg
US Naval Surface Weapons Center Dahlgren Lab
George Washington NF
Fredericksburg and Spotsylvania Battlefields Memorial NMP
Staunton
George Washington Birthplace NM
Charlottesville
Fort A P Hill
Lake Moomaw
Jefferson NF
Blue Ridge Parkway
Rappahannock NWR
Wallops Island NWR
NASA Wallops Flight Center
Covington
Lexington
George Washington NF
Richmond
Bluestone Lake
Jefferson National Forest
Lynchburg
James
Petersburg Federal Correctional Institution
Presquile NWR
Camp Peary
Appomattox Court House NHP
Fort Lee
Petersburg
James River NWR
Colonial NHP
Eastern Shore of Virginia NWR
North Fork Pound Lake
John W Flanagan Reservoir
Blacksburg
Roanoke
Blue Ridge Parkway
Petersburg NB
Jefferson NF
Booker T Washington NM
Fort Pickett (Closed)
Fort Eustis
Plum Tree Island NWR
Langley AFB
Jefferson National Forest
Clinch River
Wytheville
Radford Army Ammunition Plant
Blue Ridge Parkway
Naval Base Norfolk
Norfolk
Marion
Craney Island Disposal Area
Jefferson NF
Philpott Lake
Cumberland Gap NHP
Bristol
Jefferson NF
Mount Rogers NRA
Martinsville
South Boston
John H Kerr Reservoir
Emporia
Suffolk
Oceana NAS
Back Bay NWR
South Holston Lake
Galax
Danville
Great Dismal Swamp NWR
Fentress Field
Mackay Island NWR
Naval Facility Engineering Command
Chesapeake Bay

Credits

THE AUTHOR

Colleen Kelly Mellor taught successfully, for 30 years, and her students ranged from those in kindergarten through grade 12. Upon retirement, she went on to a successful 8-year stint as realtor but left it, to do what she always wanted to do—write stories.

Her work has been published in the ***Wall Street Journal***, ***Scripps-Howard***, the ***Providence Journal, NY Times*** and CNN-acclaimed medical blog, kevinMD.com.

Today, she writes "Encouragement in a Difficult World: Biddy Bytes Blog" at www.biddybytes.com, to give a message of hope to those who struggle with life crises.

While Ms. Mellor's "Grandpa and the Truck" stories are her first foray into writing children's stories, she notes she's had a lifetime honing her craft before anyone's arguably toughest audience—adolescents.

Now using her skills as story-teller, she breathes life into the exciting adventures of her husband, long-haul trucker Paul Wesley Gates, enabling children to appreciate the rich heritage of our great land and its people, as well as tell the significant contributions of truckers everywhere, as they move the big rigs against often-impossible odds.

THE TRUCKER BEHIND THE STORIES

Paul Wesley Gates, "Gater" on his CB radio, says he was born on a cotton field in Arkansas, 'so far back in the boonies, they had to pipe in sunshine.' This man became a legend in the trucking industry, driving millions of miles across the United States for 30 years. He was so good he became one of the company's "Elite Fleet" of truckers.

Today, he's 'Grandpa.' Over the years, he told his stories to his wife and she told them to their grandchildren—3 little boys who always clamored for another "Grandpa and the Truck" story.

They loved hearing how Grandpa battled tough road conditions, awful weather, fatigue, and crazy drivers, as he moved households and goods across America.

He now shares his stories so all children may 'ride high,' in the big rig, seeing our beautiful country, meeting fascinating people who taught him amazing life lessons.

THE ILLUSTRATOR

Dana Irwin is an Asheville, NC-based designer/illustrator who began her publishing career in New York, NY, at Hearst Magazines. She was Art Director for San Francisco-based Northern CA Home & Garden Magazine, after which she became Art and Photography Director for Lark Books, Asheville, NC.

She now freelances her design and illustration work through Irwin Design, and lives with her two dogs and two cats.

18836199R00017

Made in the USA
Lexington, KY
27 November 2012